rockschool®

POPULAR MUSIC THEORY

Workbook

GRADE 2

www.rslawards.com

Acknowledgements

Published by Rockschool Ltd. © 2015
Catalogue Number RSK011505
ISBN: 978-1-908920-71-3

Publishing

Written, compiled and edited by Simon Troup, Jennie Troup and Stuart Slater.
Internal design and layout by Simon and Jennie Troup, Digital Music Art.
Cover designed by Philip Millard, Philip Millard Design.
Additional proofing by Chris Bird, Owen Bailey, Nik Preston, Mike Stylianou, Joanna Taman and Mary Keene.

Syllabus Consultants

Rachael Meech, Mike Stylianou, Joanna Taman and Anna Cook.

Contributors

Prof. Joe Bennett, Simon Niblock, Jonathan Preiss, Stefan Redtenbacher, Philip Henderson and Martin Hibbert.

Images & Illustrations

pp. 20 & 44 | © iStock.com/craftvision
p. 20 | © iStock.com/sumnersgraphicsinc
p. 21 | © iStock.com/rapideye
pp. 23 & 46 | © grmarc / Shutterstock.com
pp. 23 & 46 | © mitay20 / Shutterstock.com
p. 45 | © iStock.com/graffizone

Distribution

Exclusive Distributors: Hal Leonard

Contacting Rockschool

www.rslawards.com
Telephone: +44 (0)845 460 4747
Email: info@rslawards.com

Table of Contents

Introductions & Information

Page

Theory Exam Sections

Page

Sample Paper

Page

Additional Information

Page

Welcome to Rockschool Popular Music Theory – Grade 2

Rockschool publish two sets of books to help candidates prepare for theory examinations – the *Rockschool Popular Music Theory Guidebooks* and *Rockschool Popular Music Theory Workbooks.*

The guidebooks are a teaching resource for candidates to work through the material required for the Rockschool theory syllabus with the support of their teacher.

To complement the guidebooks, a set of workbooks provide a series of exercises and sample papers in which to practise the skills introduced in the guidebooks.

Entering Rockschool Examinations

It's now easier than ever to enter a Rockschool examination. Simply go to *www.rslawards.com/enter-online* to book your exam online today.

Syllabus Content Overview

An overview of the syllabus content covered at this grade can be found at the back of this book. As this is a cumulative syllabus, you can download overviews for all grades from the Rockschool website at *www.rslawards.com/theory* along with other theory syllabus related resources.

Exam Format

The exam has four sections. These are:

- **Music Notation** (20%)
  In this section, all questions relate to music notation.

- **Popular Music Harmony** (25%)
  In this section, all questions relate to music harmony.

- **Band Knowledge** (25%)
  This section is in two parts, with each part covering a range of instruments:
    – **Part 1:** Identification
    – **Part 2:** Notation and Techniques

- **Band Analysis** (30%)
  In this section, the questions will include the identification of music notation, harmony and the stylistic characteristics of drums, guitar, bass, keys and vocals in a multi-instrumental context.

SECTION 1 | MUSIC NOTATION

SUMMARY	
SECTION *(Current section highlighted)*	MARKS
> **Music Notation**	**20 [20%]**
Popular Music Harmony	25 [25%]
Band Knowledge	25 [25%]
Band Analysis	30 [30%]

The *Music Notation* section of Rockschool Theory Examinations covers the following:

- 1.1 Pitch
- 1.2 Note length/rhythm
- 1.3 Dynamics, articulations and phrasing

You will be presented with a variety of exercises to hone your understanding and skills in these areas within the content specified for this grade.

Content Overview

An overview of the syllabus content covered at this grade can be found at the back of this book. As this is a cumulative syllabus, you can download overviews for all grades from the Rockschool website at *www.rslawards.com*.

Section 1 | Music Notation

Note lengths | Adding barlines

1. Add barlines to the following stave, ensuring that there are the correct number of beats in each bar:

2. Add barlines to the following stave, ensuring that there are the correct number of beats in each bar:

3. Add barlines to the following stave, ensuring that there are the correct number of beats in each bar:

Note lengths | Add the time signature

1. Add the correct time signature to the start of the following stave:

2. Add the correct time signature to the start of the following stave:

3. Add the correct time signature to the start of the following stave:

Note lengths | Add the missing notes

1. Add a note of the correct length above each question mark so that each bar matches the time signature:

2. Add a note of the correct length above each question mark so that each bar matches the time signature:

3. Add a note of the correct length above each question mark so that each bar matches the time signature:

Note lengths | Beaming notes

1. Rewrite the music from bar 1 into bar 2, connecting the notes with beams where appropriate:

2. Rewrite the music from bar 1 into bar 2, connecting the notes with beams where appropriate:

3. Rewrite the music from bar 1 into bar 2, connecting the notes with beams where appropriate:

Section 1 | Music Notation

Note lengths | Adding together note and rest values

1. Add together the value of the notes and rests on the left, then write a single note of the same pitch and total value on the right:

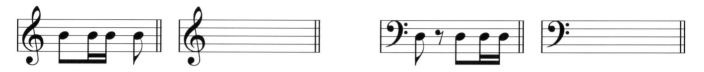

2. Add together the value of the notes and rests on the left, then write a single note of the same pitch and total value on the right:

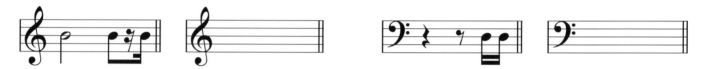

3. Add together the value of the notes and rests on the left, then write a single note of the same pitch and total value on the right:

Note lengths | Equivalent notes and rests

1. For every note there is an equivalent rest. Complete the following pairs by drawing the equivalent note or rest in the empty bars on the right:

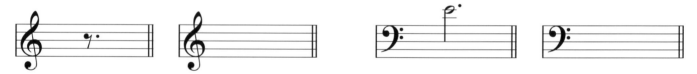

2. For every note there is an equivalent rest. Complete the following pairs by drawing the equivalent note or rest in the empty bars on the right:

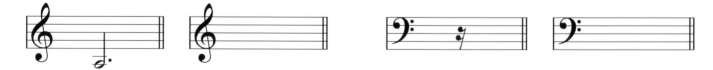

3. For every note there is an equivalent rest. Complete the following pairs by drawing the equivalent note or rest in the empty bars on the right:

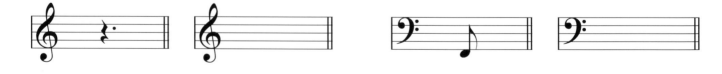

Note names | Adding the correct clef

1. Add the correct clef to the beginning of the stave below to make a major scale. Finally, tick the correct scale name in the box below the stave:

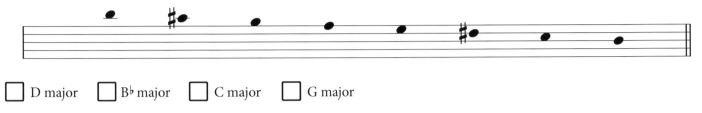

☐ D major   ☐ B♭ major   ☐ C major   ☐ G major

2. Add the correct clef to the beginning of the stave below to make a major scale. Finally, tick the correct scale name in the box below the stave:

☐ F major   ☐ B♭ major   ☐ D major   ☐ G major

3. Add the correct clef to the beginning of the stave below to make a major scale. Finally, tick the correct scale name in the box below the stave:

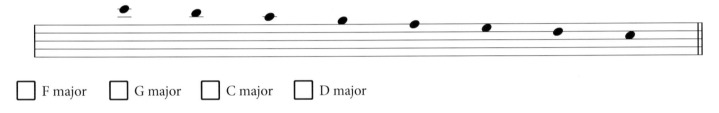

☐ F major   ☐ G major   ☐ C major   ☐ D major

Note names | Identifying chords

1. Circle the three consecutive notes that form the B♭ major chord in the stave below. This happens only once:

2. Circle the three consecutive notes that form the D major chord in the stave below. This happens only once:

3. Circle the three consecutive notes that form the G major chord in the stave below. This happens only once:

Section 1 | Music Notation

Repeats | Understanding 1st and 2nd time repeats

1. Compare the three musical examples below:

Example A

Example B

Example C

Example A uses repeat markings, whereas examples B and C are written out in full. Which version (B or C) accurately matches example A? *(Tick one box)*

◻ Example B matches A   ◻ Example C matches A

2. Compare the three musical examples below:

Example A

Example B

Example C

Example A uses repeat markings, whereas examples B and C are written out in full. Which version (B or C) accurately matches example A? *(Tick one box)*

◻ Example B matches A   ◻ Example C matches A

Dynamics & Articulations | Identifying dynamics

1. Answer the questions below relating to the following passage of music:

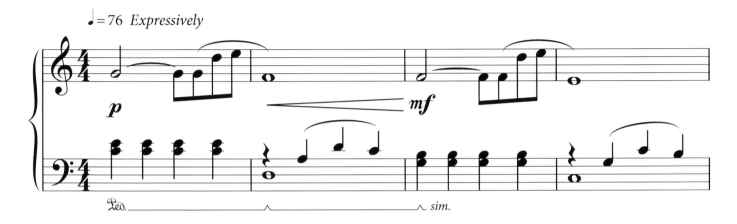

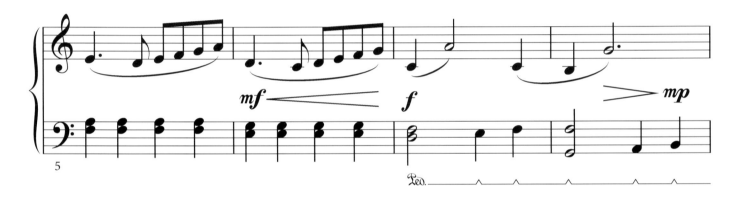

Which bar or bars contain a crescendo?

....

Which bar is played loudly throughout?

....

Which bar or bars contain a diminuendo?

....

Which bar is the quietest?

....

Which bar contains the musical symbol mezzo-piano?

....

Section 1 | Music Notation

Dynamics & Articulations | Identifying dynamics

1. Write a musical symbol in each box that represents one of the following dynamic levels, ensuring that they are arranged from quietest to loudest as directed by the arrow:

loud
moderately quiet
quiet
moderately loud

Quietest ⟶ Loudest

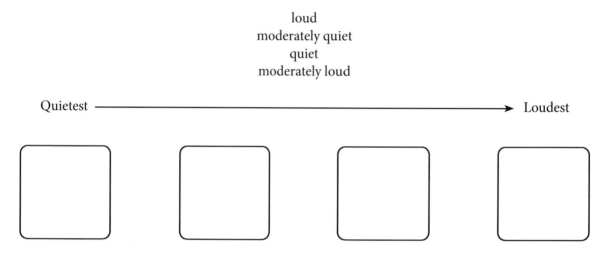

Dynamics & Articulations | Identifying articulations

1. Complete the blank spaces in the table below with information relating to the articulations attached to the notes in the column on the left:

SYMBOL	NAME OF ARTICULATION	MEANING
♩.		
♩ >		Emphasise the note
♩ ♩ ♩ (slur)	Slur/Legato	

Section 2 | Popular Music Harmony

The *Popular Music Harmony* section of Rockschool Theory Examinations covers the following:

- 2.1 Scales and related intervals
- 2.2 Simple triadic chords

You will be presented with a variety of exercises to hone your understanding and skills in these areas within the content specified for this grade.

Content Overview

An overview of the syllabus content covered at this grade can be found at the back of this book. As this is a cumulative syllabus, you can download overviews for all grades from the Rockschool website at *www.rslawards.com*.

Section 2 | Popular Music Harmony

Intervals | Identifying major and minor thirds

1. Identify the following melodic intervals by ticking the correct box below each example:

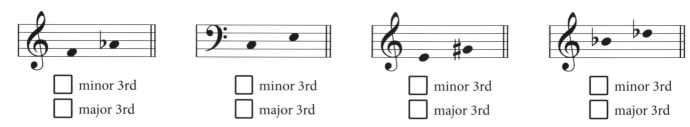

☐ minor 3rd   ☐ minor 3rd   ☐ minor 3rd   ☐ minor 3rd
☐ major 3rd   ☐ major 3rd   ☐ major 3rd   ☐ major 3rd

2. Add a note a major 3rd higher to the right of each of the following notes:

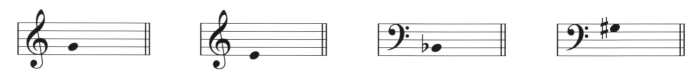

3. Add a note a minor 3rd higher to the right of each of the following notes:

Intervals | Identifying major and minor thirds

1. Circle the two consecutive notes which are a major 3rd apart. This happens only once:

2. Circle the two consecutive notes which are a minor 3rd apart. This happens only once:

3. Circle the two consecutive notes which are a major 3rd apart. This happens only once:

And when the time has come that I should move on,

Scales | Identifying scale intervals

1. Write 'T' in boxes between notes that are a **T**one apart, and write 'S' in boxes between notes that are a **S**emitone apart:

A natural minor

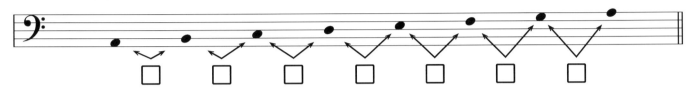

2. Write 'T' in boxes between notes that are a **T**one apart, and write 'S' in boxes between notes that are a **S**emitone apart:

G natural minor

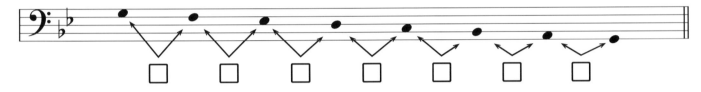

3. Write 'T' in boxes between notes that are a **T**one apart, and write 'S' in boxes between notes that are a **S**emitone apart:

G major

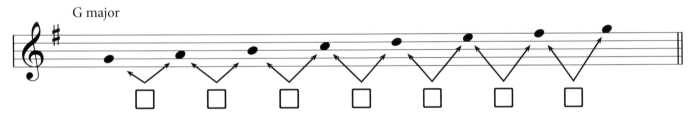

Scales | Writing scales with accidentals

1. Using whole notes, write a one-octave *descending* scale of D major. Do *not* use a key signature; instead, add accidentals where necessary:

2. Using whole notes, write a one-octave *ascending* scale of B natural minor. Do *not* use a key signature; instead, add accidentals where necessary:

3. Using whole notes, write a one-octave *descending* scale of F major. Do *not* use a key signature; instead, add accidentals where necessary:

Section 2 | Popular Music Harmony

Scales | Applying scale knowledge

1. Are there any wrong notes in this B natural minor scale?

   B   C♯   D   E   F♯   G   A   B

   ☐ Yes   ☐ No

2. Put circles around any notes that are **not** in the B♭ major scale:

   A♭   B♭   C   D   E♭   F♯   G   A   B   C   D

3. Write out the letter names (with their accidentals if appropriate) of the D natural minor scale:

   Your answer: ....

4. One or more accidentals are missing from this G natural minor scale. Underline any wrong notes and add their accidentals:

   G   A   B   C   D   E   F   G

5. Are there any wrong notes in this A natural minor scale?

   A   B   C   D   E   F   G   A

   ☐ Yes   ☐ No

6. Look at each note in turn, circling those that can be found in the D major scale:

   F♯   B   C   B♭   G♮   E   D   C♯   F   A   D♭   A♮   G   E♮

7. Briefly describe the function of a 'sharp' sign:

   Your answer: ....

Arpeggios | Identifying arpeggios

1. This is a D minor *ascending* and *descending* arpeggio. Add the correct clef and the D minor key signature:

2. This is a B♭ major *ascending* and *descending* arpeggio. Add the correct clef and the B♭ major key signature:

3. This is an E minor *ascending* and *descending* arpeggio. Add the correct clef and the E minor key signature:

4. Using whole notes, complete the stave below by adding the notes of a one-octave *ascending* and *descending* arpeggio in the **major** key shown by the clef and key signature:

5. Using whole notes, complete the stave below by adding the notes of a one-octave *ascending* and *descending* arpeggio in the **minor** key shown by the clef and key signature:

6. Using whole notes, complete the stave below by adding the notes of a one-octave *ascending* and *descending* arpeggio in the **minor** key shown by the clef and key signature:

Section 2 | Popular Music Harmony

Chords | Applying chord knowledge

1. Add the name of each chord on the line below each stave. Finally, using your knowledge of chords and the principle of relative major and relative minor keys, draw lines connecting each chord on the left with its counterpart on the right. For example, an A minor chord should be connected to a C major chord because their keys are related:

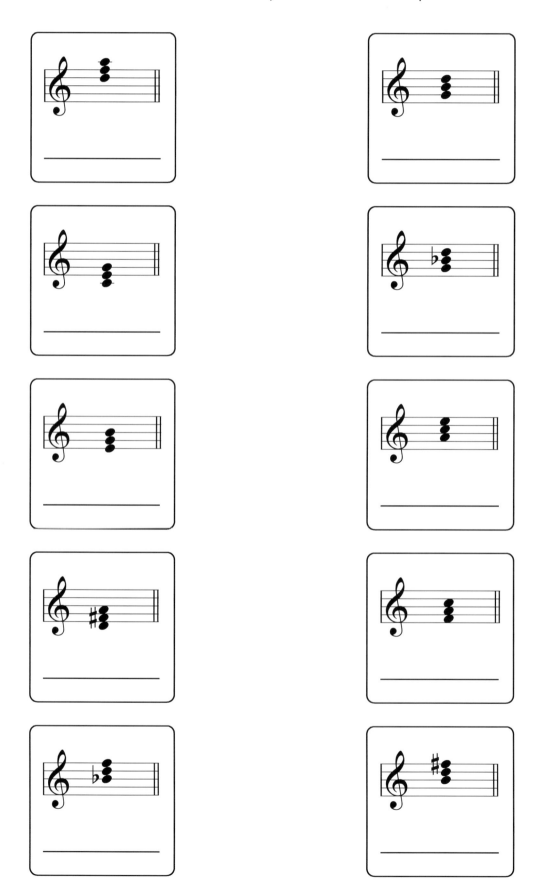

SECTION 3 | BAND KNOWLEDGE

SUMMARY

SECTION (Current section highlighted)	MARKS
Music Notation	20 [20%]
Popular Music Harmony	25 [25%]
> **Band Knowledge**	**25 [25%]**
Band Analysis	30 [30%]

The *Band Knowledge* section of Rockschool Theory Examinations covers the following:

- 3.1 Identify instrument parts and function
- 3.2 Identify instrument-specific notation
- 3.3 Identify instrumental techniques

You will be presented with a variety of exercises to hone your understanding and skills in these areas within the content specified for this grade.

Content Overview
An overview of the syllabus content covered at this grade can be found at the back of this book. As this is a cumulative syllabus, you can download overviews for all grades from the Rockschool website at *www.rslawards.com*.

Section 3 | Band Knowledge

Part 1 | Identification | Drums

The following question refers to the labelled image of a drum kit on the right:

1. Write a letter name in each box to identify the correct parts of the drum kit as shown in the labelled image:

   ☐ Snare drum   ☐ Hi-hat

   ☐ Crash   ☐ Ride

   ☐ Bass drum   ☐ Toms

The following question refers to the labelled image of a snare drum on the right:

2. Tick the box of the letter which correctly identifies the drum head:

   ☐ A   ☐ B

   ☐ C   ☐ D

   ☐ E   ☐ F

True or false:

3. The bass drum, toms and snare drum are always tuned to the same pitch: ☐ True   ☐ False

4. A hi-hat consists of two cymbals: ☐ True   ☐ False

5. Toms are usually mounted on the hi-hat stand: ☐ True   ☐ False

6. Tick the boxes of any drum-kit parts that are operated by a foot pedal:

   ☐ Hi-hat   ☐ Ride   ☐ Crash   ☐ Toms   ☐ Snare drum   ☐ Bass drum

7. Which type of cymbal is usually placed on the drummer's right-hand side and often used for rhythmic work? *(Tick one box)*

   ☐ Hi-hat   ☐ Ride   ☐ Crash

Part 1 | Identification | Guitar and Bass

The following question refers to the labelled image below:

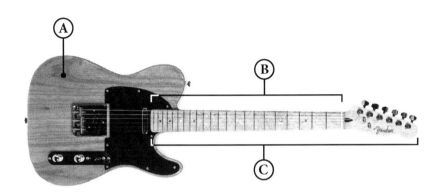

1. Write a letter name in each box below to correctly identify the parts of the guitar as shown in the image above:

   ☐ Body   ☐ Neck   ☐ Fretboard

True or false:

2. A fret is a thin, raised metal bar embedded into the fingerboard of a guitar: ☐ True   ☐ False

3. Guitar fretboards are usually made from metal: ☐ True   ☐ False

4. Frets are moved up and down the neck a little to play in different keys: ☐ True   ☐ False

---

The following descriptions below form the options for the questions that follow:

A) Metal strips placed across the width of the neck.
B) The largest and widest part of the guitar.
C) A piece of wood embedded with metal strips. The strings are pushed down against this.

5. Which statement best describes the fretboard? *(Tick one box)*

   ☐ A   ☐ B   ☐ C

6. Which statement best describes a fret? *(Tick one box)*

   ☐ A   ☐ B   ☐ C

7. Which statement best describes the guitar body? *(Tick one box)*

   ☐ A   ☐ B   ☐ C

Section 3 | Band Knowledge

Part 1 | Identification | Keys

True or false:

1. A sustain pedal is also called a soft pedal:

   ☐ True   ☐ False

2. A sustain pedal is used to let the notes ring on until the pedal is released and the note dies away naturally:

   ☐ True   ☐ False

3. A soft pedal on a piano changes the volume:

   ☐ True   ☐ False

4. A soft pedal on a piano alters the pitch:

   ☐ True   ☐ False

The following two statements describe the use of two different keyboard pedals. Match the statements with the pedal names.

5. This pedal on a piano reduces the volume. On an electronic keyboard it can also change other effects such as pitch or vibrato. It is sometimes called the modulation pedal: *(Tick one box)*

   ☐ Sustain pedal   ☐ Soft pedal

6. This pedal can be used to play legato by allowing the sound to continue: *(Tick one box)*

   ☐ Sustain pedal   ☐ Soft pedal

----

7. Tick the checkboxes of the following notes if they are white keys:

   ☐ A   ☐ B   ☐ C♭   ☐ D   ☐ E♯   ☐ F♯   ☐ G♭

8. Tick the checkboxes of the following notes if they are black keys:

   ☐ C   ☐ D♯   ☐ E♯   ☐ F   ☐ G   ☐ A♭   ☐ B♯

Part 1 | Identification | Vocals

The following four questions refer to the labelled illustration on the right:

1. Which letter points to the trachea? *(Tick one box)*

   ☐ A ☐ B ☐ C ☐ D ☐ E

2. Which letter points to the tongue? *(Tick one box)*

   ☐ A ☐ B ☐ C ☐ D ☐ E

3. Which letter points to the lips? *(Tick one box)*

   ☐ A ☐ B ☐ C ☐ D ☐ E

4. Which letter points to the lungs? *(Tick one box)*

   ☐ A ☐ B ☐ C ☐ D ☐ E

Fill in the blanks:

5. The _____ and _____ are essential tools for a singer to form and articulate lyrics.

6. When you sing, you have to drop your _____ to open your mouth wide.

7. When you inhale, your _____ expand and fill with air.

True or false:

8. Moving the position of your tongue within your mouth has no effect on the sound produced during singing:

   ☐ True   ☐ False

Part 2 | Notation & Techniques | Drums

The following three questions relate to the one-bar extract of drum notation below:

1. Which drum voice plays on every beat within the bar? *(Tick one box)*

   ☐ Hi-hat   ☐ Crash   ☐ Ride   ☐ Toms   ☐ Bass drum   ☐ Snare drum

2. Which two drum voices play on the final beat of the bar? *(Tick two boxes)*

   ☐ Hi-hat   ☐ Crash   ☐ Ride   ☐ Toms   ☐ Bass drum   ☐ Snare drum

3. Which drum voices do not play at all in this extract? *(Tick one or more boxes)*

   ☐ Hi-hat   ☐ Crash   ☐ Ride   ☐ Toms   ☐ Bass drum   ☐ Snare drum

---

The following four questions relate to the two-bar extract of drum notation below:

True or false:

4. The technique used on the fourth beat of the first bar is called a flam:

   ☐ True   ☐ False

5. The hi-hat remains open throughout the second bar:

   ☐ True   ☐ False

6. The toms are played in bar 1 only:

   ☐ True   ☐ False

7. The final note in the second bar is played on the ride cymbal:

   ☐ True   ☐ False

Part 2 | Notation & Techniques | Guitar and Bass

The following two questions relate to the two-bar extract of guitar notation on the right:

1. In the first bar, what does the PM mean? *(Tick one box)*

   ☐ Palm mute   ☐ Pick mute   ☐ Pull mute

2. Which performance technique is used in the second bar? *(Tick one box)*

   ☐ Staccato   ☐ Pull-off   ☐ Slide

In this section, you are asked to add notation symbols to the musical extract on the right:

3. Add the correct symbol to show a pull-off should be played from the first note of the bar to the second note of the bar.

4. Add the correct symbol to show that, following on from the third note, the fourth note is a hammer-on.

5. Add the correct symbol to show that there is a slide between the final two notes.

True or false:

6. The instruction *let ring* tells the guitarist to play the string with a particular finger:

   ☐ True   ☐ False

7. The instruction *hammer-on* tells the guitarist to sound the note by forcefully striking down on the fret with a finger rather than plucking or picking the string:

   ☐ True   ☐ False

8. The instruction *slide* is also called a *pull-off*:

   ☐ True   ☐ False

Section 3 | Band Knowledge

Part 2 | Notation & Techniques | Keyboards

The following four questions relate to the two-bar extract of keyboard notation on the right:

1. Which beat contains a marking suggesting that the notes are to be played legato? *(Tick one box)*

   ☐ Beat 1   ☐ Beat 2   ☐ Beat 3   ☐ Beat 4

2. In which beat are the notes accented? *(Tick one box)*

   ☐ Beat 1   ☐ Beat 2   ☐ Beat 3   ☐ Beat 4

3. In which beat do you find tenuto marks? *(Tick one box)*

   ☐ Beat 1   ☐ Beat 2   ☐ Beat 3   ☐ Beat 4

4. Which hand plays the upper stave? *(Tick one box)*

   ☐ Left hand   ☐ Right hand

- -

5. In most music, which hand tends to play the melodies? *(Tick one box)*

   ☐ Right hand   ☐ Left hand

6. Which musical symbol indicates that a passage should be played legato? *(Tick one box)*

   ☐ Dot   ☐ Hairpin   ☐ Slur   ☐ Short flat line

7. Which hand tends to play in the bass clef? *(Tick one box)*

   ☐ Right hand   ☐ Left hand

8. Does an accent indicate that a note should be played louder or softer? *(Tick one box)*

   ☐ Louder   ☐ Softer

9. Which of the following marks indicates that a note should be held for its full rhythmic value? *(Tick one box)*

   ☐ Accent   ☐ Slur   ☐ Dot   ☐ Tenuto

Part 2 | Notation & Techniques | Vocals

The following three questions relate to the one-bar extract of vocal notation on the right:

1. What are the short lines between some of the lyrics called? *(Tick one box)*

   ☐ Syllables   ☐ Hyphens   ☐ Trachea

2. What does the long, diagonal line between the last two notes indicate? *(Tick one box)*

   ☐ Legato   ☐ Portamento   ☐ Falsetto

3. Which clef is being used in this musical extract? *(Tick one box)*

   ☐ Treble   ☐ Alto   ☐ Tenor   ☐ Bass

Some-times when you're smil - ing

In this section, you are asked to add notation symbols to the musical extract on the right:

4. Add staccato symbols over the final two notes.

5. Place a portamento symbol between the first two notes.

6. Add any missing hyphens.

Dream-ing   of   our   sum   mer

True or false:

7. An alto singer has a lower pitch range than a tenor: ☐ True   ☐ False

8. An alto singer can usually sing higher than a tenor: ☐ True   ☐ False

9. A soprano singer has a higher pitch range than an alto: ☐ True   ☐ False

10. Soprano and alto are usually female vocal ranges: ☐ True   ☐ False

11. Notes with a staccato symbol should be sung smoothly: ☐ True   ☐ False

12. Portamento is another way of describing a pitch slide: ☐ True   ☐ False

13. Tenor is the lower of the female vocal ranges: ☐ True   ☐ False

Band Analysis

The *Band Analysis* section of Rockschool Theory Examinations covers the following:

- 4.1 Identify general music features
- 4.2 Accurately complete a score
- 4.3 Identify instrument-specific techniques and stylistic traits

You will be presented with a variety of exercises to hone your understanding and skills in these areas within the content specified for this grade.

Content Overview

An overview of the syllabus content covered at this grade can be found at the back of this book. As this is a cumulative syllabus, you can download overviews for all grades from the Rockschool website at *www.rslawards.com*.

Section 4 | Band Analysis

Band Analysis | Example 1

The following 12 questions relate to the four-bar score below. Note that bar 4 has blank areas to be filled in as part of the tasks below:

1. What key is this piece in?

    Your answer: ....

2. Briefly describe the information given to you in the tempo marking:

    Your answer: ....

    ....

    ....

3. Place a G major chord symbol over the first beat of the bar that starts with two eighth-note chords of G major.

4. In bar 2, add a symbol to show that the guitar chords should be palm-muted throughout the bar.

5. Name the pitch of the lowest note played by the guitar in this piece:

    Your answer: ....

6. Which two drum voices are played at the same time that the guitar plays a half-note chord?

   Your answer:

7. In bar 1, beat 2 of the bass-guitar part, there is a small note written before the quarter note. What is this type of note called?

   Your answer:

8. What note is played in the bass-guitar part when the guitar plays an accented chord?

   Your answer:

9. In which bar do all three instruments play a decrescendo? *(Tick one box)*

   ☐ Bar 1   ☐ Bar 2   ☐ Bar 3   ☐ Bar 4

10. Add the missing bass-guitar part in the final bar of the score, as indicated below:

    Beats 1 & 2:   Four eighth notes, the pitch of each note should be B (on the stave).
    Beat 3:   Quarter note, the pitch should be E (below the stave).
    Beat 4:   Quarter-note rest.

11. Add drum notation to the drum part in beats 1 & 2 of the final bar of the score, as indicated below:

    Beat 1:   An eighth-note bass drum followed by an eighth-note high tom.
    Beat 2:   An eighth-note mid tom followed by an eighth-note low tom.

12. The style of this piece is rock. From the following list, identify three features from the score that are typically found in this style: *(Tick three boxes, and add the name of the instrument for each box you tick)*

    ☐ Eighth notes played on root notes   Instrument: ....

    ☐ Octave unison   Instrument: ....

    ☐ Powerchord progression   Instrument: ....

    ☐ Backbeat groove   Instrument: ....

    ☐ Walking bassline   Instrument: ....

    ☐ Triads played in eighth notes   Instrument: ....

Section 4 | Band Analysis

Band Analysis | Example 2

The following 13 questions relate to the four-bar score below. Note that bar 3 has blank areas to be filled in as part of the tasks below:

1. What key is this piece in?

   Your answer: ....

2. What is the tempo of this piece?

   Your answer: ....

   ....

3. In bar 1, which two drum voices are heard when the piano part has quarter-note rests?

   Your answer: ....

4. In the same bar as the hi-hat is played open, add an indication to show that the bass-guitar part should be palm muted throughout the bar.

5. Write the correct chord name over the first chord played in bar 1.

6. Write the correct chord name over the first chord played in bar 3.

7. What type of cymbal is played when all the other parts are playing a half note?

   Your answer: ....

8. In the right hand of the piano part, name the melodic interval formed between the first two eighth notes of bar 2:

   Your answer: ....

9. Name the harmonic interval formed by the two half notes on beat 3 of bar 4 in the piano part:

   Your answer: ....

10. In bar 4, add the correct dynamic markings to all three parts to indicate the following information:

    Beat 1:   The music is played moderately loudly.
    Beats 1 & 2: The music increases in volume.
    Beat 3:   The music is played loudly.

11. In bars 1 & 3, the bass guitar plays a bassline at the same time as the piano plays chords. At which point does the bass guitar play notes that are *not* the root note of the chord being played by the piano? *(Tick one box)*

    ☐ Bar 1, beats 1 & 2   ☐ Bar 1, beats 3 & 4   ☐ Bar 3, beats 1 & 2   ☐ Bar 3, beats 3 & 4

12. Add a left-hand piano part to bar 3. The rhythm should match the right-hand part, and the pitch should be the root notes of the two chords played in the right hand.

13. The style of this piece is pop. From the following list, identify three features from the score that are typically found in this style: *(Tick three boxes, and add the name of the instrument for each box you tick)*

    ☐ Backbeat groove   Instrument: ....

    ☐ Walking bassline   Instrument: ....

    ☐ Eighth notes played on root notes Instrument: ....

    ☐ Octave unison   Instrument: ....

    ☐ Powerchord progression   Instrument: ....

    ☐ Eighth note snare drum/tom fill   Instrument: ....

Section 4 | Band Analysis

Band Analysis | Example 3

The following 12 questions relate to the four-bar score below. Note that bar 2 has blank areas to be filled in as part of the tasks below:

1. What key is this piece in?

   Your answer: ....

2. Briefly describe the information given to you in the time signature:

   Your answer: ....

   ....

   ....

3. Add chord symbols above bars 1 & 2 of the guitar part.

4. Name the drum technique used on the snare drum in beats 2–4 of bar 3.

5. In bar 1, which two drum voices play when the bass guitar has rests? *(Tick two boxes)*

   ☐ Bass drum   ☐ Hi-hat   ☐ Crash   ☐ Ride   ☐ Snare drum

6. Circle the highest-pitched note in the score.

7. Describe the meaning of the dynamic markings in bar 3:

Your answer: ....

....

8. In which bar or bars do all three instruments play loudly throughout the bar? *(Tick one or more boxes)*

☐ Bar 1   ☐ Bar 2   ☐ Bar 3   ☐ Bar 4

9. What is the combined value of the rests in bar 2 of the guitar part? *(Tick one box)*

☐ 1 beat   ☐ 1½ beats   ☐ 2 beats   ☐ 2½ beats   ☐ 3 beats

10. Add the missing bass-guitar part in bar 2. Use the same rhythm pattern as the guitar part above, and use the pitches from the root notes of the guitar chords, transposed down to an appropriate octave for the bass guitar.

11. Add an accent to the longest note played by the bass guitar in the score.

12. The style of this piece is metal. Name two musical devices found in the score which are typical of this style, and name the instrument in which they appear:

Your answer: ....

....

....

....

....

....

SAMPLE PAPER

The following pages contain examples of the types of questions you will find in a Grade 2 exam paper. They give an indication of the content, format, layout and level at this grade.

You will see the exam paper has been split into the same four sections that have been presented earlier in this workbook:

- Music Notation
- Popular Music Harmony
- Band Knowledge
- Band Analysis

Content Overview
- **Marking:**
  - The exam is marked out of a total of 100, and the total available marks for each section are clearly stated at the start of each section. There is also a blank markbox where your total examination score can be noted.
  - The total marks available for each question are displayed on the right, and include a space for your teacher to mark your answers.

- **General advice:**
  - If a question requires a written answer, don't feel compelled to use every line. Answering the question correctly is much more important than using all the available space.
  - Aim to answer all the questions set. If you get stuck on one particular question, move on and come back to it later.

- **Neatness:**
  - Your answers should be neat, accurate and legible as marks cannot be given if your response is ambiguous.
  - Avoid unnecessary corrections by thinking your responses through before committing them to paper.
  - Use a pencil that is sharp enough to write precisely, but soft enough to rub out and make corrections.
  - To avoid confusion, tick boxes (checkboxes) should be marked with a clear tick symbol rather than a cross. Please note that some answers require more than one box to be ticked, so read the questions carefully.

Please visit *www.rslawards.com* for detailed information on all Rockschool examinations, including syllabus guides, marking schemes and examination entry information.

Grade 2 | Sample Paper

Section 1 | Music Notation

Total marks for this section: 20

Mark:

Q 1.01 | Identify the missing time signature: *(Tick one box)*   `1`

☐ $\frac{2}{4}$ ☐ $\frac{3}{4}$ ☐ $\frac{4}{4}$

Q 1.02 | Identify the missing time signature: *(Tick one box)*   `1`

☐ $\frac{2}{4}$ ☐ $\frac{3}{4}$ ☐ $\frac{4}{4}$

Q 1.03 | Identify the missing note as indicated with a question mark: *(Tick one box)*   `1`

☐ ♩   ☐ ♩.   ☐ ♪.   ☐ ♪

Q 1.04 | Identify the missing rest as indicated with a question mark: *(Tick one box)*   `1`

☐ 𝄽.   ☐ 𝄾.   ☐ 𝄾   ☐ 𝄿

Q 1.05 | Add the three note values together and identify the matching note value from the options below: *(Tick one box)*   **| 1 |**

☐ 𝅝   ☐ 𝅝·   ☐ 𝅗𝅥   ☐ 𝅗𝅥·

Q 1.06 | Add the three note values together and identify the matching note value from the options below: *(Tick one box)*   **| 1 |**

☐ 𝅘𝅥·   ☐ 𝅘𝅥   ☐ 𝅗𝅥·   ☐ 𝅗𝅥

Q 1.07 | Which note has the same value as the written rest? *(Tick one box)*   **| 1 |**

☐ 𝅘𝅥   ☐ 𝅘𝅥𝅮   ☐ 𝅘𝅥𝅯   ☐ 𝅘𝅥𝅮·

Q 1.08 | Which rest has the same value as the written note? *(Tick one box)*   **| 1 |**

☐ 𝄽·   ☐ 𝄼·   ☐ 𝄼·   ☐ 𝄾·

Q 1.09 | Identify the missing clef and the correct scale name: *(Tick two boxes)* [2]

☐ Treble clef ☐ Bass clef

☐ D major ☐ B♭ major ☐ F major ☐ G major

Q 1.10 | Identify the missing clef and the correct scale name: *(Tick two boxes)* [2]

☐ Treble clef ☐ Bass clef

☐ D major ☐ B♭ major ☐ F major ☐ G major

Q 1.11 | What is the full name and meaning of the ***mp*** dynamic marking? *(Tick one box)* [1]

☐ Mezzo piano (moderately quiet) ☐ Molto piano (very quiet) ☐ Meno piano (less quiet)

Q 1.12 | Which is the correct musical term for the following symbol? *(Tick one box)* [1]

☐ Staccato ☐ Accent ☐ Legato ☐ Crescendo

Q 1.13 | Which is the correct symbol for the musical term 'crescendo'? *(Tick one box)* [1]

☐ > ☐ *f* ☐ < ☐ ⌒

Q 1.14 | Circle the three consecutive notes that form the D major chord in the stave below:

Q 1.15 | Write down the sequence of letters that represents the order in which the following bars are played from the start to the finish:

Your answer: ....

Grade 2 | Sample Paper

Section 2 | Popular Music Harmony

Total marks for this section: 25

Mark:

Q 2.01 | Write 'S' in the boxes between notes that are a Semitone apart:

2

Q 2.02 | Add a note to the right of each of the notes to create the requested melodic interval:

3

Major 2nd   Major 3rd   Minor 3rd

Q 2.03 | Using whole notes, write a one-octave *ascending* scale of B♭ major. Do not use a key signature; instead, add accidentals if needed:

5

Q 2.04 | Using whole notes, write a one-octave *ascending* scale of D major. Add the correct key signature if needed:

5

Q 2.05 | Using whole notes, complete the stave below by adding the notes of a one-octave *ascending* and *descending* arpeggio in the **major** key shown by the clef and key signature:

5

Q 2.06 | Circle the group of three notes that form a D major chord:

| 1 |

D B C   G B D   D F♯ A   G F♯ A   D C♯ E

Q 2.07 | Circle the group of three notes that form a B♭ major chord:

| 1 |

B♭ D E♭   B D F   B♭ D F   C E♭ F   B♭ G D

Q 2.08 | Circle the group of three notes that form a G major chord:

| 1 |

G A B   F B G   G B F♯   G B E   G B D

Q 2.09 | Circle the major chord that shares its name with the key indicated by the key signature and clef.
Finally, add the chord name on the line below the stave:

| 2 |

Your answer: ....

Section 3 | Band Knowledge | Part 1 – Identification

The following three questions refer to the labelled image of a drum kit on the right:

Q 3.01 | Which letter corresponds to the snare drum?

1

Your answer: ....

Q 3.02 | Which letter corresponds to the floor tom?

1

Your answer: ....

Q 3.03 | What is the name of the drum labelled 'H'?

1

Your answer: ....

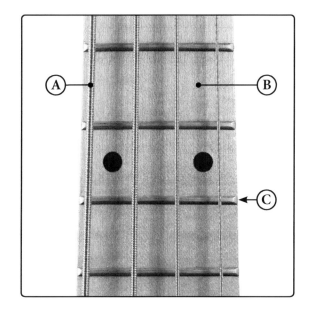

The following three questions refer to the image on the right:

Q 3.04 | What is the correct name for the part of the instrument labelled 'A'?   1

Your answer: ....

Q 3.05 | What is the correct name for the part of the instrument labelled 'B'?   1

Your answer: ....

Q 3.06 | What type of instrument is shown in the image?   1

Your answer: ....

Q 3.07 | How many strings does a standard guitar have?   1

Your answer: ....

Q 3.08 | On a piano with two pedals, what is the name of the pedal on the left?   1

Your answer: ....

Q 3.09 | On a piano, what is the name of the pedal that can be used to play legato by allowing the sound to continue?

| 1 |

Your answer: ....

Q 3.10 | What colour is the key of the note B flat on a piano keyboard?

| 1 |

Your answer: ....

The following three questions refer to the labelled image on the right:

Q 3.11 | Which letter points to the lungs? *(Tick one box)*

| 1 |

☐ A   ☐ B   ☐ C   ☐ D   ☐ E

Q 3.12 | Which letter points to the tongue? *(Tick one box)*

| 1 |

☐ A   ☐ B   ☐ C   ☐ D   ☐ E

Q 3.13 | Which letter points to the trachea? *(Tick one box)*

| 1 |

☐ A   ☐ B   ☐ C   ☐ D   ☐ E

Section 3 | Band Knowledge | Part 2 – Notation & Techniques

The following three questions relate to the one-bar extract of drum notation on the right:

Q 3.14 | Which drum voice plays with the bass drum on the first beat of the bar? *(Tick one box)* ☐ 1

☐ Hi-hat ☐ Crash ☐ Ride ☐ Toms ☐ Snare drum

Q 3.15 | On which beat of the bar is there a flam? ☐ 1

Your answer: ....

Q 3.16 | Which cymbal is not played in this extract? *(Tick one box)* ☐ 1

☐ Crash ☐ Ride ☐ Hi-hat

The following three questions relate to the one-bar extract of guitar notation on the right:

Q 3.17 | On the first beat of the bar, what does PM mean? *(Tick one box)* ☐ 1

☐ Play muted ☐ Pick mute ☐ Palm mute ☐ Passing mute

Q 3.18 | What is the name of the technique used on the first four notes of the bar (as indicated with a dot below the note heads)? *(Tick one box)* ☐ 1

☐ Slide ☐ Staccato ☐ Pull-off ☐ Hammer-on

Q 3.19 | What technique is used on the third beat of the bar (as indicated with a line between the two notes)? *(Tick one box)* ☐ 1

☐ A slide between the two notes ☐ Hammer on the second note ☐ Mute both notes

The following three questions relate to the one-bar extract of piano music on the right:

Q 3.20 | In which beat is there an accented chord? *(Tick one box)* ☐ 1

☐ 1   ☐ 2   ☐ 3   ☐ 4

Q 3.21 | In which beat are there tenuto marks? *(Tick one box)* ☐ 1

☐ 1   ☐ 2   ☐ 3   ☐ 4

Q 3.22 | Which hand or hands are playing the accompaniment? ☐ 1

Your answer: ....

- -

The following three questions relate to the three-bar extract of vocal notation below:

and   now   you   know   that   I   can't   help   lov - ing   you,   yeah,__   yeah.

Q 3.23 | In which bar can you find notes that are to be sung with a portamento? ☐ 1

Your answer: ....

Q 3.24 | In which bar can you find notes that are to be sung staccato? ☐ 1

Your answer: ....

Q 3.25 | Why is the lyric "lov-ing" hyphenated? *(Tick one box)* ☐ 1

☐ Because it is sung more slowly.   ☐ Because the word has more than one syllable.

☐ Because the words are spoken.   ☐ Because the word is sung with a tenuto.

Section 4 | Band Analysis

The following 12 questions relate to the four-bar score below. Note that bar 4 has blank areas that are to be filled in as part of the tasks that follow:

Grade 2 | Sample Paper

Q 4.01 | Name the key used in this piece:

1

Your answer: ....

Q 4.02 | What is the tempo of this piece?

1

Your answer: ....

Q 4.03 | In bar 2 write the correct chord name over beats 1 & 3:

2

Q 4.04 | Circle the lowest note in the score.

1

Q 4.05 | In the bass part, add the missing notes in bar 4 as follows:

5

Four eighth notes followed by a half note, using the root notes of the chords played in the piano part.

Q 4.06 | Which part, or parts, play the longest note in bar 1? *(Tick one box)*

2

☐ Vocals   ☐ Piano   ☐ Bass guitar

☐ Vocals and piano   ☐ Vocals and bass guitar   ☐ Piano and bass guitar

Q 4.07 | In bar 2, add accents to any of the seven notes in the vocal part which are *not* a note from the chords in the piano part.

4

Q 4.08 | Add symbols to show that the piano part gradually builds in volume throughout bar 1, until it reaches a loud volume at the start of bar 2.

2

Q 4.09 | What are the two minor chords used in this piece?

2

Your answer: ....

Q 4.10 | In the bar that only contains minor chords, add an indication to the bass-guitar part telling the player to palm mute all the notes.

2

Q 4.11 | Complete bar 4 of the piano part by adding a note a minor 3rd above the last note of the left-hand part. This should be a single note of the correct length to fill the missing beats of the bar.

2

Q 4.12 | The style of this piece is pop. From the following list, identify three features in the score that are typically found in this style: *(Tick three boxes, adding the name of the instrument in which it features for each box you tick)*

6

- ☐ Powerchords   Instrument: ....
- ☐ Backbeat groove   Instrument: ....
- ☐ Scalic melody   Instrument: ....
- ☐ Walking bassline   Instrument: ....
- ☐ Eighth notes on root notes   Instrument: ....
- ☐ Triads in quarter notes   Instrument: ....

Syllabus Content Overview | Grade 2

Important: This table represents content that is new at this grade. The content of Rockschool Theory Examinations is cumulative, so Grades 1 to 8 include all content from previous grades in the syllabus. A full version of this table is available online at *www.rslawards.com*, and includes details of content at every grade.

Section	Content	Details
1: Music Notation (20%)	1.1: Pitch	note range: bass clef (C2–E4), treble clef (A3–C5)
	1.2: Note length/rhythm	note lengths: 16th notes, grace notes
		1st & 2nd time endings, repeats, anacrusis
	1.3: Dynamics, articulations, phrasing	dynamics: mezzo-piano, mezzo-forte
		articulations: tenuto
2: Popular Music Harmony (25%)	2.1: Scales and related intervals	major scales: D, B♭
		relative major/minor relationship
		natural minor scale
		natural minor scales: Am, Em, Bm, Dm, Gm
		harmonic and melodic intervals: minor 3rd
	2.2: Simple triadic chords	major chords: D, B♭
		major arpeggios: D, B♭
		minor chord formula
		minor chords: Am, Em, Bm, Dm, Gm
		minor arpeggios: Am, Em, Bm, Dm, Gm
3: Band Knowledge (25%)	3.1: Identify instrument parts and function	drums: high, mid, low toms
		guitar and bass guitar: fretboard, frets
		keys: soft pedal, sustain pedal
		vocals: tongue, lips
	3.2: Identify instrument-specific notation	drum notation: high, mid, low toms, flams
		guitar and bass-guitar notation: hammer-on, palm mutes, arpeggiated chords, let ring
		keys notation: accents, tenuto
		vocal notation: hyphens between syllables, use of second line of lyrics for second verse
	3.3: Identify instrumental techniques	as listed above in 3.2
4: Band Analysis (30%)	4.1: Identify general music features listed within criteria 1, 2 and 3 within a score	identify and show understanding of the applied musical elements listed within the first three sections (above) within the context of a score
		instrument range: drums (hi-hat, snare drum, bass drum, crash cymbal, ride cymbal, toms), guitar, bass guitar, keyboard, vocals
		number of parts: 3
		piece length: 4 bars
	4.2: Accurately complete a score	1 bar, within any part: rhythm, pitch, chord names, articulations, dynamics, tempo
	4.3: Identify instrument-specific techniques and stylistic traits	as listed within part 3 (above)
		identify musical and stylistic devices used within the score (pop, blues, rock, metal, funk)

rockschool®

ENTER ONLINE

Ready to take your Rockschool Theory Exam?

Now it's easier than ever...

1 GO TO WWW.RSLAWARDS.COM/ENTER-ONLINE

2 CREATE AN ACCOUNT

3 SELECT YOUR EXAM CENTRE AND DATE

4 CHOOSE YOUR GRADE

... and you're ready to go.

Book your exam today – go to **www.rslawards.com/enter-online**, or email **info@rslawards.com** for more information.